S0-ADG-207

WONDER WOMAN

VOL.1 THE LIES

WONDER WOMAN
VOL.1 THE LIES

GREG RUCKA
writer

LIAM SHARP
artist

MATTHEW CLARK
penciller (pages 7-26)

SEAN PARSONS
inker (pages 7-26)

LAURA MARTIN
JEREMY COLWELL
colorists

JODI WYNNE
letterer

LIAM SHARP & LAURA MARTIN
collection and original series cover artists

Special thanks to Paulo Siqueira

WONDER WOMAN created by WILLIAM MOULTON MARSTON

CHRIS CONROY MARK DOYLE Editors – Original Series ✴ **DAVE WIELGOSZ** Assistant Editor – Original Series ✴ **JEB WOODARD** Group Editor – Collected Editions
ROBIN WILDMAN Editor – Collected Edition ✴ **STEVE COOK** Design Director – Books ✴ **LOUIS PRANDI** Publication Design

BOB HARRAS Senior VP – Editor-in-Chief, DC Comics

DIANE NELSON President ✴ **DAN DiDIO** Publisher ✴ **JIM LEE** Publisher ✴ **GEOFF JOHNS** President & Chief Creative Officer
AMIT DESAI Executive VP – Business & Marketing Strategy, Direct to Consumer & Global Franchise Management
SAM ADES Senior VP – Direct to Consumer ✴ **BOBBIE CHASE** VP – Talent Development ✴ **MARK CHIARELLO** Senior VP – Art, Design & Collected Editions
JOHN CUNNINGHAM Senior VP – Sales & Trade Marketing ✴ **ANNE DePIES** Senior VP – Business Strategy, Finance & Administration
DON FALLETTI VP – Manufacturing Operations ✴ **LAWRENCE GANEM** VP – Editorial Administration & Talent Relations ✴ **ALISON GILL** Senior VP – Manufacturing & Operations
HANK KANALZ Senior VP – Editorial Strategy & Administration ✴ **JAY KOGAN** VP – Legal Affairs ✴ **THOMAS LOFTUS** VP – Business Affairs ✴ **JACK MAHAN** VP – Business Affairs
NICK J. NAPOLITANO VP – Manufacturing Administration ✴ **EDDIE SCANNELL** VP – Consumer Marketing ✴ **COURTNEY SIMMONS** Senior VP – Publicity & Communications
JIM (SKI) SOKOLOWSKI VP – Comic Book Specialty Sales & Trade Marketing ✴ **NANCY SPEARS** VP – Mass, Book, Digital Sales & Trade Marketing

WONDER WOMAN VOLUME 1: THE LIES

Published by DC Comics. Compilation and all new material Copyright © 2017 DC Comics. All Rights Reserved. Originally published in single magazine form in
WONDER WOMAN: REBIRTH 1, WONDER WOMAN 1, 3, 5, 7, 9, 11. Copyright © 2016 DC Comics. All Rights Reserved. All characters, their distinctive likenesses and related
elements featured in this publication are trademarks of DC Comics. The stories, characters and incidents featured in this publication are entirely fictional.
DC Comics does not read or accept unsolicited submissions of ideas, stories or artwork.

WB Shield TM and © Warner Bros. Entertainment Inc.

DC Comics, 2900 West Alameda Ave., Burbank, CA 91505
Printed by LSC Communications, Salem, VA, USA. 1/20/17. First Printing.
ISBN: 978-1-4012-6778-0
Barnes & Noble exclusive edition ISBN: 978-1-4012-7635-5

Library of Congress Cataloging-in-Publication Data is available.

PEFC Certified

Printed on paper from
sustainably managed
forests, controlled
sources

PEFC/29-31-337   www.pefc.org

SOMETHING'S HAPPENING...IN MY *MEMORY*...
THE *STORY* KEEPS *CHANGING*.

THE QUEEN OF THE AMAZONS WISHED FOR A DAUGHTER UNTIL SHE WAS *SURE* HER HEART WOULD *SHATTER* FOR THE WANT OF THE CHILD.

AND THE GODS ANSWERED, AND TOLD HER A BABY GIRL WOULD BE HERS, FASHIONED FROM CLAY AND SAND AND MADE REAL BY THEIR WILL.

OR.

THE QUEEN OF THE AMAZONS FELL IN *LOVE*, AND THE MAN SHE CHOSE WAS *WORTHY* OF HER HEART, HER EQUAL ON THE FIELD OF BATTLE AND OFF IT, AS WELL.

AND HE WAS NOT A MAN AT ALL, BUT IN *TRUTH* WAS THE RULER OF OLYMPUS, AND SO BY *ZEUS* THE QUEEN CAME TO BE WITH CHILD.

OR *CHILDREN*.

AND INTO *PARADISE* THERE WAS BORN A *DAUGHTER*.

AND THE QUEEN NAMED THE PRINCESS *DIANA*...

...AND THE WORLD, NEVER HAVING SEEN HER LIKE BEFORE, CALLED HER *WONDER WOMAN*.

I HAVE BEEN CALLED SO **MANY** THINGS, BY SO MANY PEOPLE.

SOME **FLATTER**.

MANY **INSULT**.

FEW ARE **ACCURATE**.

WONDER.

WOMAN.

I REMEMBER BELIEVING THAT "WONDER" MEANT *"AWE."*

THAT THE NAME THEY GAVE ME SPOKE OF *ADMIRATION.*

PERHAPS IT DID, ONCE.

BUT THE STORY KEEPS CHANGING.

THAT'S **NOT** WHAT THEY MEAN WHEN THEY CALL ME "WONDER."

NOT ANYMORE. PERHAPS NOT **EVER.**

IT'S **THEIR** WORD, NOT MINE.

THEY **WONDER.**

WHAT IS THAT? **HOW** CAN SUCH A WOMAN **EXIST?**

•LIVE

WHO IS SHE?

•LIVE

THE TRUTH IS, I NO LONGER *KNOW.*

THE TRUTH...

...MATTERS....

OR I *THINK* IT DOES.

OR PERHAPS IT DID *ONCE,* AND DOES *NO LONGER.*

OR PERHAPS IT *NEVER* DID.

BUT THAT SEEMS... *WRONG.*

IT *SHOULD* MATTER. IT SHOULD MATTER A *GREAT DEAL.*

OR PERHAPS IT SHOULDN'T. THE STORY KEEPS *CHANGING.*

THIS IS THE *HELM* OF THE *GOD* OF *WAR.* WORN BY *ARES,* WON BY *ME.*

I *THINK* I AM THE GOD OF WAR.

YET I THINK THAT *CANNOT* BE TRUE.

WAR...

...THE *FIRST* CASUALTY OF WAR...

...IS *TRUTH.*

ONCE A DAUGHTER WAS BORN TO THE QUEEN OF THE AMAZONS, AND AS THE AMAZONS DID NOT **AGE**, SHE WAS THE DAUGHTER OF THEM **ALL**.

...SHE WAS BUT ONE CHILD AMONG MANY, YET VIEWED WITH **SUSPICION** AND **SCORN**, MOCKED FOR BEING **LESS** THAN HER SISTERS.

CALLED **UNNATURAL**, OF **NO** MOTHER, AND MADE FROM CLAY.

THEY LOVED HER, AND TAUGHT HER ALL THEY KNEW, SHARING THEIR **KNOWLEDGE** AND **WISDOM**.

SHE KNEW SHE WAS **DIFFERENT**, BUT THAT WAS NOT CAUSE FOR SHAME, BUT CELEBRATION.

OR...

SHE KNEW SHE WAS **DIFFERENT**, AND WAS MADE ASHAMED, AND SHE DID NOT BELIEVE HER HOME WAS **PARADISE**...

...AND THEN PARADISE WAS **BREACHED** FOR THE FIRST TIME IN **MILLENNIA**.

A DYING **SAILOR** BROUGHT BY THE GODS TO THEIR SHORES.

OR...

...AN UNWITTING **HERALD** WITH A **DIRE** MESSAGE...

...THAT ARES WOULD BREAK HIS **CHAINS** TO UNLEASH MADNESS UPON **ALL** THE WORLD.

AND EVEN THE WALLS OF PARADISE WOULD **CRUMBLE**, AND THE AMAZONS, TOO, WOULD DROWN IN THE GOD OF WAR'S UNENDING FRENZY FOR **BLOOD**.

THE QUEEN **HEARD** THE MESSAGE THE GODS HAD DELIVERED, AND SHE **UNDERSTOOD**, AND THUS SHE **ANSWERED**.

THEMYSCIRA WOULD CHOOSE A **CHAMPION** TO RETURN THE SAILOR HOME, TO **FIGHT** ALONGSIDE THE WORLD OF MEN, AND END THE **MADNESS OF ARES.**

THIS CHAMPION WOULD SACRIFICE HER **ETERNAL YOUTH,** HER HOME, HER PLACE AMONGST HER **FRIENDS** AND **FAMILY.**

NOT **ONE** OF THE AMAZONS HESITATED FOR A MOMENT TO MAKE THIS SACRIFICE...

...OR PERHAPS ONE DID...

...PERHAPS THE QUEEN COULD NOT **BEAR** THE THOUGHT OF LOSING THE DAUGHTER SHE HAD LONGED FOR, AND FORBADE HER THE TRIALS...

...YET IN THE END IT WAS THE PRINCESS WHO **PROVED** HERSELF OVER HER SISTERS.

IT WAS THE PRINCESS WHO WOULD BE THEMYSCIRA'S **CHAMPION,** WHO WOULD **LEAVE** HER HOME...

...BELIEVING SHE WOULD NEVER-- **COULD** NEVER-- RETURN.

AND SO THE PRINCESS CAME TO THE WORLD OF MEN.

THE FIRST CASUALTY OF WAR IS THE *TRUTH*.

AND THE TRUTH *DOES* MATTER.

IT USED TO BE THE *ONLY* THING THAT *MATTERED*.

WHO AM I?

WONDER WOMAN.

NO. *MORE*.

THE *WHOLE* TRUTH.

YOU ARE DIANA, PRINCESS, DAUGHTER OF HIPPOLYTA, TENTH QUEEN OF THE AMAZONS.

VERY WELL.

FOOL.

AND I CANNOT FOR THE LIFE OF ME THINK OF WHERE IT WENT **WRONG**.

THE MOMENT WHEN WHO I **WAS** AND WHO I **AM** BECAME SO TERRIBLY DIVIDED.

THE MOMENT WHEN I **LOST** MYSELF.

THE MOMENT WHEN I **FORGOT** WHO I WAS.

BUT MY **VISION** IS CLEARING.

THE HUNTER LEARNS THE LESSON **EARLY**.

TO FOLLOW THE **SIGNS**, LEST ONE BECOMES **LOST**.

AND IF ONE BECOMES LOST, YOU MUST **STOP**.

PAUSE. CONSIDER.

THEN RETRACE YOUR **STEPS** WITH CARE.

FIND WHERE YOU STEPPED **WRONG**.

FIND THE **SOURCE** OF THE **DECEPTION**.

OLYMPUS. NOW.

LIKE SPOTTING A **CRACK** IN AN AMPHORA OR HEARING A WRONG **NOTE** IN A TUNE...

...AND **NOW** I CANNOT HELP BUT SEE THE **FLAWS** IN THE WORLD AROUND ME.

HOST OF OLYMPUS!

IS THIS HOW YOU GREET ONE OF YOUR OWN?

OR HAS **THAT** LIE BEEN LAID BARE, **TOO?**

AUTOMATONS.

THESE ONES ARE **SENTRIES**, WITHOUT **REASON** OR **THOUGHT**.

THE WORK OF HEPHAESTUS.

THEY CAN DO **ONLY** AS THEY HAVE BEEN **INSTRUCTED**, NO MORE AND NO LESS.

NO REMORSE, NOR HESITATION. NO REGRET, NOR CONSCIENCE.

AND THE[Y] WILL **NEV**[ER] RELENT.

WHEN A LIE IS **CONFRONTED,** THERE ARE THREE CHOICES.

ADMISSION, AND THUS **HONESTY.**

PERPETUATION AND THUS **FEEBLE** DECE

IT'S MY *PREFERENCE* TO GIVE *THREE* WARNINGS.

THIS IS YOUR *FIRST:*

SORRY I'M LATE.

WHERE'VE YOU BEEN?

TRAFFIC ON THE *BELTWAY*, THEN A MEETING WITH THE *DIRECTOR*.

WHERE ARE THEY NOW?

TRACKING *CADULO'S* MEN OUTSIDE *TESSANA*.

GOOD MORNING, TOMAS.

GOOD MORNING, COMMANDER.

NUMBER?

THEY COUNT EIGHTEEN.

AND ARMED?

Oh, YEAH.

THERE'S SOMETHING *ELSE*.

WE'VE GOT A REPORT THAT *WONDER WOMAN* WAS SEEN ENTERING *BWUNDAN* AIRSPACE JUST AFTER DAWN, LOCAL.

STILL TRYING TO *VERIFY*.

IT *COULD* BE COINCIDENCE.

Commander
Etta O. Candy

--STRAIGHT, YOU'RE ASKING IF I COMPROMISED OPERATIONAL SECURITY?

YOU'VE GOT A LONG HISTORY WITH HER, STEVE.

SO DO YOU, ETTA!

IF SHE'S IN-COUNTRY, IT'S NOTHING TO DO WITH US.

CADULO IS PRECISELY THE KIND OF PROBLEM SHE LOOKS TO SOLVE.

I'M SAYING I WOULD UNDERSTAND IF YOU'D LEAKED IT TO HER.

WELL, I DIDN'T, I WOULDN'T...

...AND DIANA AND I HAVEN'T SPOKEN IN A LONG TIME, NOW, ALL RIGHT?

ALL RIGHT.

PICKET OUT.

SERIOUSLY, STEVE, THERE'S LIKE, A MILLION BETTER PHOTOS ON THE INTERNET...

...YOU GOTTA GET A BETTER PICTURE OF HER, MAN!

YEAH, I KNOW DAVY...

...THING IS, THIS ONE'S MINE.

FACE ME!

TALK TO ME!

I DID NOT ASK FOR THIS FIGHT!

ONLY THAT YOU LISTEN!

...THE BOUDA ARE THE **DEVOTED** OF **URZKARTAGA.** THEY THINK ME A **GODDESS...**

...SO I SUPPOSE THAT MAKES **TWO** OF US.

NOT ANYMORE. PERHAPS I NEVER **WAS,** I NO LONGER KNOW.

NOT WHAT I HEARRRD.

WHATEVER THE **TRUTH,** OLYMPUS IS NOW **CLOSED** TO ME.

BUT MORE... I HAVE **LOST** THE WAY TO THEMYSCIRA.

Tch. THE PRRETTY PRRRRINCESS CAN'T GO **HOME** AGAIN?

AND YOU WANT ME TO HELP YOU FIND YOURRR WAY, IS THAT IT?

YES.

NO.

BARBARA ANN, PLEASE... I AM ASKING FOR YOUR **HELP** ONCE **MORE.**

YOU **DARE?!**

THE **WAY** YOU HELPED **ME,** YOU MEAN?

THE WAY YOU LET URRZKARRRTAGA **USE** ME? TURRRN ME INTO **THIS?**

HIS **CURRRSSSED** BRIDE, HIS **UNFAITHFUL** WIFE--

HISSSSS

--WE SHOULD MOVE.

TRRRY TO KEEP UP.

BY THE GODS--

--HAVEN'T YOU BEASTS DONE ENOUGH?

RRRROOOOOAAARRRRR

RRRRR--

GET AWAY FROM HER!

--I'M AN ANIMAL A BEAST--

--THAT MUST EAT MAN'S FLESH TO LIVE--

YOU CAN!

--MYSELF--

YOU'RE STRONGER THAN HIM!

YOU ARE NO BEAST--

...YOU ARE MY FRIEND!

--ALL THE TIME--

--PUNISHING ME...

--HE MAKES ME, HE MAKES ME--

--YOU ARE A WOMAN...

--HUNGRRRY ALL THE TIME--

...BECAUSE HE WAS NOT MY FIRRRST...

NO...

...ALL THE TIME HUNGRRRY ALL THE TIME...

...THAT IS NOT WHY HE PUNISHES YOU.

THAT IS NEVER WHY ANY LIKE HIM DO.

THEY DO IT BECAUSE THEY CAN.

OKAY, YOU WIN.

YES, MA'AM.

SO WE'VE LOST TREVOR'S TEAM, AND OUR INTEL SAYS THAT CADULO'S *APOTHEOSIS* COULD HAPPEN AT *ANY MOMENT.*

I ASSUME YOU'RE HERE BECAUSE YOU WANT PERMISSION TO MOUNT A *RESCUE* OPERATION?

ACTUALLY, NO.

NO?

WONDER WOMAN WAS TRACKED ENTERING BWUNDAN AIRSPACE YESTERDAY, LAST SEEN IN THE BANAKANE RAINFOREST.

THAT'S THREE HUNDRED KILOMETERS *SOUTH* OF ECHO TEAM'S LAST-KNOWN.

I KNOW.

YOU THINK SHE'S IN BWUNDA BECAUSE OF CADULO? OR BECAUSE OF TREVOR?

I HONESTLY DON'T HAVE THE FIRST IDEA WHY SHE'S THERE.

BUT IT'S NOT COINCIDENCE.

IF STEVE'S IN TROUBLE, IF HIS *TEAM* IS IN TROUBLE, SHE'LL BE THERE FOR THEM.

THAT PRESUMES THAT WONDER WOMAN *KNOWS* MASTER CHIEF TREVOR IS IN *TROUBLE,* ETTA.

SHE DOESN'T *NEED* TO KNOW. IT DOESN'T... *WORK* LIKE THAT WITH THEM...

JUST **MEN.** WEAK. MORTAL.

ANTS BENEATH THE FOOT OF A **GIANT.**

THERE'S A TECHNICAL TERM FOR THAT.

"ILLEISM."

"ILLEISM," THANKS, DAVY. SOME CONSIDER IT A SIGN OF **NARCISSISM** OR EVEN **MEGALOMANIA.**

I'M MAYBE GOING OUT ON A **LIMB,** BUT MY MONEY'S ON MEGALOMANIA.

Heh.

THIS IS **INTERESTING.**

WHO IS SHE TO **YOU?**

WONDER WOMAN.

YOUR *HUNGER*... IT'S GOTTEN *WORSE.*

LIKE A *LUST* THAT CAN NEVERRR BE *QUENCHED.* YET ANOTHER OF URZKARTAGA'S *JOKES* AT MY EXPENSE.

DO YOU *KNOW* WHAT IT'S *LIKE* TO HAVE A *GOD* ON YOUR NECK?

CONTRRROLLING WHAT YOU *FEEL,* WHAT YOU *THINK?*

I SUPPOSE YOU DO.

I AM LOSING THE MEMORY OF WHO I *WAS,* DIANA.

"DOCTORRR BARRRBARRRA ANN MINERRRVA...

"...SHE WAS *WORRRTHY,* ONCE."

SHE STILL IS. *YOU* STILL *ARE.*

Hah! ALL THAT YOU HAVE *ENDURRRED,* EVERRRYTHING YOU HAVE *SEEN,* AND STILL YOU INSIST ON BELIEVING THE *BEST* OF ME.

I REMEMBER YOUR *KINDNESS* WHEN WE FIRST *MET.*

YOU WAR WITH YOUR BETTER ANGELS, AND ALWAYS HAVE.

AND I REMEMBER WHEN YOU COULDN'T TURN A *PHRASE* LIKE A *POET.*

THAT WAS A VERY **INTERESTING** MEETING WITH COMMANDER CANDY, SASHA.

YOU DID THAT **VERY** WELL.

THANK YOU, DOCTOR.

CADULO'S COMPROMISED, BUT WE KNEW THAT WOULD HAPPEN.

WE'RE ACCELERATING THE TIMETABLE. INITIATE **PHASE TWO.**

PHASE TWO REQUIRES THE AMAZON.

CORRECT...

...FORTUNATELY FOR US, TREVOR AND CANDY ARE ABOUT TO **DELIVER** WONDER WOMAN TO US ON A **PLATTER**....

IS THIS **ALL** OF THEM?

WE'RE MISSING ABOUT A **DOZEN**, BY MY **COUNT**. THIS ISN'T JUST **ONE** VILLAGE'S DAUGHTERS, DIANA.

CADULO MUST'VE BEEN **ABDUCTING** GIRLS FROM ALL OVER THE **REGION**.

WHY IS THE **TEAM** HERE, CHRISTOPHER?

TARGET IS A **WARLORD** NAMED **ANDRES CADULO**. HE'S TRYING TO WORK A **RITUAL** TO FREE URZKARTAGA BY GIVING HIM A **HUMAN** FORM.

THING IS, ACCORDING TO COMMANDER CANDY'S **INTEL**, CADULO CAN **DO** IT.

THAT IS WHY HE HAS YOURRR **STEVE**, PRINCESS.

HE WILL BE **CONSUMED** BY URRRZKARRTAGA.

STEVEN.

SORRY I'M *LATE*.

HEY, ANGEL.

I WASN'T WORRIED.

SO THESE GIRLS--

YES.

IF *CADULO*--

YES.

THEN URZKARTAGA--

I MAY HAVE AN IDEA ABOUT THAT.

I'VE MISSED YOU.

I'VE MISSED YOU, TOO.

DEFILER!!!

THE **WOMEN**, ALL THE **WOMEN**, THE **STORY** YOU TOLD ME--

--THEY WERE **CORRUPTED**, HE LIED!

YOU WERE **NEVER** HIS **WORSHIPPERS**--

--YOU'RE HIS **WARDENS!**

BE SILENT!

NO **WOMAN** RULES ME, **NEVER** AGAIN--

BIND HIM! YOU AND THE **GIRLS**--

--TRAPPED BY THE LIKES OF **YOU!**

I WILL BE--

--WILL--

--BE...

...NOTHING.

CADULO--

IS IN CUSTODY, MA'AM. AND *ALL* BUT SEVEN OF THE YOUNG WOMEN WHO WERE ABDUCTED HAVE BEEN RETURNED TO THEIR *FAMILIES.*

WHY ALL BUT SEVEN?

THEY HAVE ASSUMED THE SACRED DUTY OF *GUARDING* AGAINST THE GOD'S *RETURN.*

I LOOK FORWARD TO READING YOUR AFTER-ACTION REPORT, MASTER CHIEF TREVOR.

THANK YOU, MA'AM.

PERHAPS YOU AND ECHO TEAM WOULD LIKE TO GET YOURSELVES SORTED?

I THINK WE WOULD LIKE TO DO THAT VERY MUCH, THANK YOU, MA'AM.

I'LL GET THIS INTO **CONTAINMENT**...

...MISTER **TREVOR?**

MA'AM?

I ASSUME **WONDER WOMAN'S** CONTRIBUTION TO THIS MISSION WILL BE DETAILED IN THE AFOREMENTIONED REPORT?

ABSOLUTELY, MA'AM. I BELIEVE IN ALWAYS GIVING **CREDIT** WHERE IT'S **DUE.**

AND WHERE IS SHE **NOW?** IF I NEED TO **SPEAK** WITH HER?

I THINK SHE AND **COMMANDER CANDY** TOOK AN **OLD** FRIEND **SHOPPING.**

YOU'RE DRAWING A **CROWD**.

PRESS?

NOT **YET**. GIVE IT TIME.

YOU REALIZE, SWEETIE, WHAT HAPPENS IF YOU ACTUALLY **BUY** ANYTHING?

...ABOUT YOUR **THEMYSCIRA** PROBLEM, AND I HAVE AN **IDEA**...

THERE **HAS** ALWAYS BEEN AN UNDUE INTEREST IN MY WARDROBE.

AND YOUR **HAIR,** THEY DO **LOVE** TO WONDER HOW YOU DO YOUR **HAIR**.

DO PEOPLE STILL TRY TO **TOUCH--**

THEY DON'T DARE.

DIANA! I'VE BEEN THINKING...

"...SHE DOES IT BECAUSE SHE KNOWS WHAT IT MEANS TO THEM THAT SHE DOES."

WASHINGTON, D.C.
EMPIRE ENTERPRISE BUILDING.

WHEN'D SHE GET BACK INTO THE COUNTRY?

FOUR-POINT-TWO HOURS AGO.

CADULO MISSION STATUS: **RESOLVED,** SUCCESSFUL.

BORDEAUX REPORTS **URZKARTAGA** HAS BEEN CONTAINED.

APPARENTLY, HE IS NOW BOUND WITHIN A **POTTED PLANT.**

WE'RE GOING TO NEED THAT.

I SHALL INITIATE **DELIVERY** AND ADVANCE PHASE TWO.

UPDATE: DR. BARBARA ANN MINERVA.

SHE HAS BEEN **CURED.**

MISSION-CRITICAL UPDATE.

REQUESTED LATEST GLOBAL **GEOSAT** DATA TO ASSIST IN INQUIRY FOR THE AMAZON.

APPARENTLY, THE AMAZON CANNOT FIND HER WAY **HOME.**

WHAT WAS **THAT?**

REPEATING: THE AMAZON **CANNOT** FIND HER WAY **HOME.**

HAVE BORDEAUX GIVE CANDY **ANYTHING** SHE NEEDS.

CONTACT ...RINA, PREP AN ...TEAM FOR **RAPID** ...OYMENT, STAGED ON **STANDBY.**

...

DONE.

ADRIANNA, **WHAT** ARE YOU **DOING?**

I THOUGHT FOR AN INSTANT I SAW...I DID! YOU'RE SMILING!

NO... N...

...HALL ...E MEDIA! ...E: EMPIRE ...ERONICA ...ILES! FILM ...LEVEN!

VERONICA CALE SMILES! World rejoices!

YOU CAN **FEEL** IT, CAN'T YOU? AFTER ALL THIS TIME, WE'RE CLOSE.

VARIABLES MAKE THE

NO, THIS IS **DIFFERENT.**

THIS TIME, WONDER WOM... IS UNDER OU... **CONTROL.**

...STARTED EIGHTH GRADE, NOW.

PLEASE TELL HER I SAID HELLO. AND MAYA.

THEY'D LOVE IT IF YOU CAME TO VISIT.

I WOULD LIKE THAT.

I'LL GO FIRST--

STEVE, I--

YOU FIRST.

NO, YOU.

I'VE MISSED YOU. I'VE MISSED YOU A LOT.

I'VE MISSED YOU, AS WELL. YOU ALWAYS KNEW HOW TO REACH ME.

I KNOW.

BUT YOU DIDN'T.

YOU HAD SOMEBODY ALREADY.

WE DO NOT ALWAYS KNOW WHY OUR HEARTS CHOOSE AS THEY DO.

IF YOU ARE ASKING WHY *HIM* AND NOT YOU, STEVE, I HAVE ASKED MYSELF THE *SAME* QUESTION.

HE'S SUPERMAN.

OR *WAS*, ANYWAY. I'M NOT REALLY *UP* ON EVERYTHING THAT'S BEEN GOING ON THERE...

...ONE TENDS TO *AVOID* GIVING TOO MUCH TIME OR ATTENTION TO THE THINGS THAT CAUSE US *PAIN*.

YES, WE DO.

BEING WITH HIM WAS...*EASY.* NO, NOT EASY. *SIMPLE.*

IT WAS, BELIEVE IT OR NOT, *UNCOMPLICATED.*

WELL, WHEN YOU *BOTH* CAN FLY....

I BELIEVE IN *LOVE,* STEVE. I KNOW THERE ARE MANY WHO THINK THAT IS *FOOLISH,* BUT I TRULY DO *BELIEVE* IN IT.

I BELIEVE WE SHOULD BE ALLOWED TO LOVE ONE ANOTHER, AND TO DO SO WITHOUT RESTRAINT.

I BELIEVE THAT LOVE IS NOT *LIMITED,* BUT *LIMITLESS.*

I AM-- PERHAPS THIS IS ARROGANT, FORGIVE ME--*GOOD AT LOVING.*

I AM NOT AS GOOD AT *ROMANCE.*

WE HAVE CIRCLED EACH OTHER FOR *YEARS.* BUT WE HAVE NEVER TRULY *TRIED,* DESPITE WHAT WE *EACH* KNOW IS IN OUR *HEARTS.*

I AM NOT AT MY *BEST,* STEVE. MY *MEMORY* IS PLAYING... TRICKS ON ME.

I FEAR I REMEMBER THINGS THAT *NEVER WERE,* AND HAVE *FORGOTTEN* THINGS THAT *ARE.*

DIANA--

BUT I HAVE *NEVER* FORGOTTEN THE SURVIVOR.

I HAVE NEVER FORGOTTEN *YOU.*

I AM NOW, AND I ALWAYS WILL BE, IN YOUR CORNER.

ANYWHERE YOU *GO,* ANYTHING YOU *DO,* ANYTHING YOU *NEED,* IT'S *YOURS.*

AS LONG AS I LIVE, DIANA.

I AM GOING TO KISS YOU NOW, STEVE.

I AM ENTIRELY OKAY WITH YOU DOING THAT, DIANA.

BRZZT BRZZT

BRZZT BRZZT

GO FOR TREVOR.

ETTA.

SHE THINKS THEY HAVE SOMETHING.

ANY IDEA WHEN WE'LL HEAR FROM THEM?

NONE. THEY *VANISHED* OFF THE MAP ALMOST FOUR *HOURS* AGO, NOTHING *SINCE* THEN.

WHICH I SUPPOSE IS A GOOD SIGN, RIGHT?

ACCORDING TO DOCTOR MINERVA, *THEMYSCIRA* DOESN'T *EXIST* IN *OUR* WORLD.

HOW *IS* SHE DOING?

HONESTLY? I'M NOT *SURE.* SHE CARRIED URZKARTAGA'S *CURSE* A LONG TIME.

NOW THAT SHE'S FREE OF IT...

I WOULD IMAGINE IT'LL TAKE SOME ADJUSTING.

BUT IF THE DOCTOR IS CORRECT, IT WOULD MAKE *SENSE* WHY WE CAN NO LONGER *FIND* MISTER TREVOR OR WONDER WOMAN.

WE'LL KNOW *MORE* IN THE MORNING, I'M SURE.

GO *HOME,* ETTA. GET SOME *REST,* TRY NOT TO *WORRY.*

YOU, AS WELL, MA'AM.

YOU GO WHERE YOU ARE *NOT* WELCOME, MALE.

MY APOLOGIES. I'M...I'M LOOKING FOR SOMEONE. FROM THE LAST TIME I WAS HERE.

I THINK HER NAME WAS--*ah*, WAIT...*CASTALIA?* THE *PRIESTESS?*

I DO NOT KNOW THE *NAME* "CASTALIA."

AND YOU SHOULD NOT WANDER *ALONE*, MALE...

...LEST MY SISTERS AND I DECIDE THAT THE *PRINCESS* NEEDS TO *SHARE* YOU...

STEVE!

DON'T THINK THAT **BELONGS** TO YOU.

SASHA--

BLAM

SKKSS
SKK
SSZZ!

I GOT IT.

I'M AFRAID, STEVE.

I KNOW.

ME, TOO.

I RODE THIS PLAIN WITH MY *HORSE*, WITH KACHI, COUNTLESS TIMES. IT DID NOT *LOOK* LIKE THIS.

WHERE THERE WAS *GRASS* NOW THERE IS *STONE*, WHERE THERE WERE *FLOWERS*, NOW THERE IS *RUBBLE*.

IT IS AS IF EVERYTHING HAS BECOME A *PARODY* OF THE *HOME* I *LEFT* BEHIND...

...AND THAT I WOULD *NEVER* RETURN TO...

THAT WAS THE *PRICE* I HAD TO PAY TO HELP YOU. TO SEE *YOUR* WORLD...

THERE WE GO.

...I HAD TO *FOREVER* LEAVE *MINE*.

OKAY, *THAT* DOESN'T LOOK GOOD. WHEN'D YOU DO THAT?

IT WAS... IT WAS *YEARS* AGO, BEFORE I *MET* YOU...

...A RIDE I HAD MADE A HUNDRED TIMES, A THOUSAND TIMES...

...AND THIS TIME, IN THE MIDDLE OF THE PLAIN, I SAW--

WONDER WOMAN

VARIANT COVER GALLERY

WONDER WOMAN #3 variant cover by FRANK CHO and NEI RUFFINO

WONDER WOMAN #7 variant cover by JENNY FRISON

WONDER WOMAN #11
variant cover by JENNY FRISON

COSTUME REDESIGN BY TONY S. DANIEL

Gold tiara with
one red star

Red cape with gold
clasp and edge

Silver forearm guards
with recessed detailing

Blue leather skirt
with gold edges
and two stars

Red knee-high boots
with gold knee guards
and accents

Previous New 52 design

PRE-SERIES TEST PAGE BY LIAM SHARP

ROUGH PENCILS TO FINAL INKS FOR WONDER WOMAN #1, PAGE 1

ROUGH PENCILS TO FINAL INKS FOR WONDER WOMAN: REBIRTH #1, PAGE 15

ROUGH PENCILS TO FINAL INKS FOR WONDER WOMAN #7 COVER